The British Museum

nosy crow

FIND TOM IN TIME

Ming Dynasty China

About Ming Dynasty China

This book takes place in China, during a time called the Ming dynasty. A dynasty is when a country is ruled by a king or **EMPEROR**, and all future rulers come from that emperor's family, until a new dynasty takes over. The Ming dynasty (1368–1644) was founded by a man called Emperor Hongwu. During this time, China became a very strong and rich country, famous for its beautiful porcelain, silk, furniture and impressive new buildings. The capital city was moved from Nanjing in the south to Beijing in the north, and the Great Wall of China was rebuilt and lengthened. Some of the places that Tom visits in this book would have been great distances apart, but they all existed during the Ming dynasty and many of them are still visited by people today.

Get ready to meet . . .

Tom

Granny Bea

Digby the cat

and spot the hidden dragon in every scene!

First published 2020 by Nosy Crow Ltd
The Crow's Nest, 14 Baden Place,
Crosby Row, London SE1 1YW
www.nosycrow.com

ISBN 978 1 78800 657 6

Nosy Crow and associated logos are trademarks
and/or registered trademarks of Nosy Crow Ltd.

Published in collaboration with the British Museum.

Text © Nosy Crow 2020
Illustrations © Fatti Burke 2020

The right of Nosy Crow to be identified as the author and Fatti Burke
to be identified as the illustrator of this work has been asserted.

A CIP catalogue record for this book is available from the British Library.

Printed in China.
Papers used by Nosy Crow are made from wood
grown in sustainable forests.

1 3 5 7 9 8 6 4 2

Contents

INTRODUCTION

Tom was an ordinary boy, most of the time.
He was clever and brave and he loved adventure.

Tom's grandmother, Bea, was an ordinary grandmother, most of the time. She was clever and brave, and a little bit mischievous, and she loved adventure, too. Which was just as well, since her job was digging in the dust and the dirt to discover how people used to live. Granny Bea was an **ARCHAEOLOGIST**.

Granny Bea's cat, Digby, did not like digging in the dust and the dirt. Or getting wet. Or missing his meals. In fact, Digby did not like adventure at all. Especially after what happened the last time Tom came to stay . . . but that's another story.

One ordinary day, Tom was at Granny Bea's house when he spotted Digby curled up on top of a beautiful green gown.

"Is that your new dressing gown, Granny Bea?" Tom asked.

"This," said Granny Bea, "is not a dressing gown. It's a young man's outfit from the Ming dynasty in China. It's around 500 years old."

"Wow!" said Tom.

"Why don't you try it on?" said Granny Bea, with a familiar twinkle in her eye.

Tom reached out for the gown, and . . . *WHOOSH!*

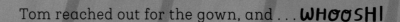

THE GREAT WALL

Tom was in Ming dynasty China!

All around him, there were workers with wheelbarrows carrying bricks and slabs of stone. They were building a long wall.

Tom looked around for Granny Bea, but she was nowhere to be found. Just then, he spotted Digby racing away!

The Great Wall of China was an incredibly long wall that was built to protect China from invaders. It took more than 2,000 years to build and hundreds of thousands of labourers, soldiers and prisoners helped to build it. Around 400,000 people died during its construction.

CAN YOU SPOT?

- A builder who has fallen asleep
- Tom
- A misbehaving ox
- Digby the cat
- Someone having a ride in a wheelbarrow
- A bird stealing someone's lunch
- A person waving from a signal tower

If any enemies tried to attack, soldiers living and working along the Great Wall would fight back with bows and arrows or **CROSSBOWS**.

During the Ming dynasty, the wall was made stronger with bricks, stone and a special **CEMENT** made from rice and lime. It was also extended and divided into nine zones, each of which was protected and maintained by soldiers living in **GARRISONS**.

THE MARKET

Tom ran after Digby until he reached a busy market. Everyone around him was wearing silk gowns like the one Granny Bea had given him.

Tom didn't want to stand out, so he quickly pulled on his gown and pushed his way through the crowds. Where had that naughty cat got to?

People bought and sold all kinds of things at the market, including fruit and vegetables, meat, tea, rice, spices, silk and **PORCELAIN**. Farmers also travelled from the countryside to buy and sell animals.

Some people sold street food at the market. They waved special hand-held drums with pellets attached to attract customers. Most sold simple food such as noodles or rice with tofu and vegetables, or sometimes a little meat.

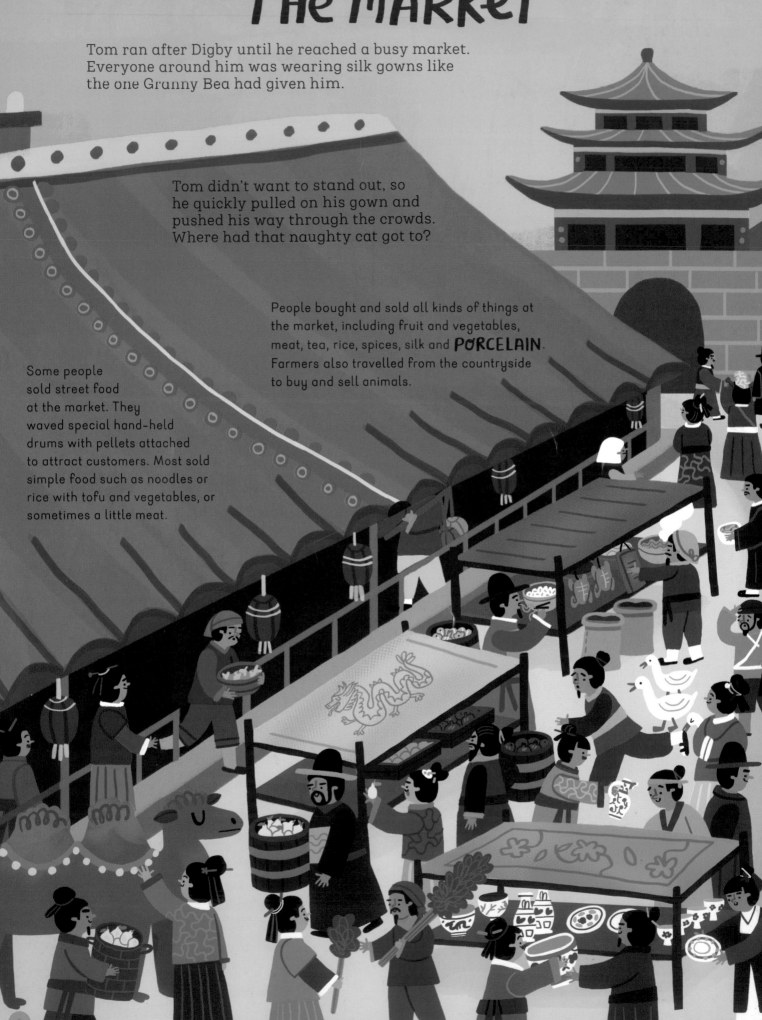

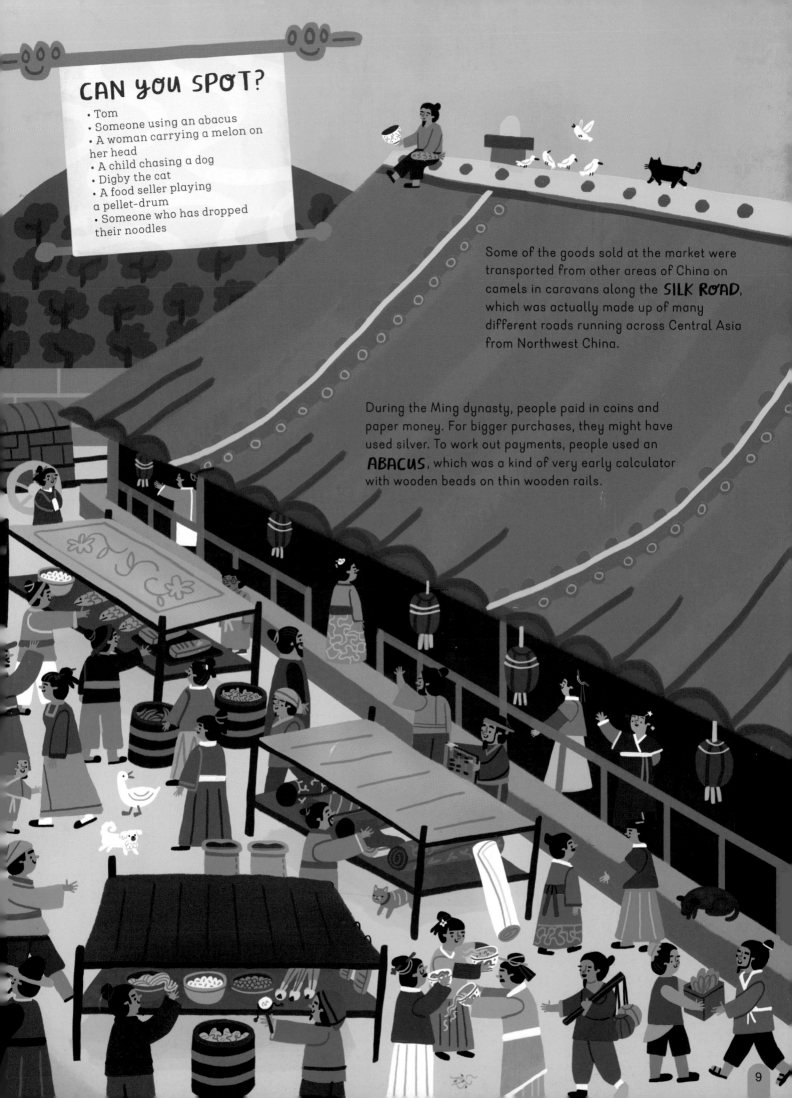

CAN YOU SPOT?

- Tom
- Someone using an abacus
- A woman carrying a melon on her head
- A child chasing a dog
- Digby the cat
- A food seller playing a pellet-drum
- Someone who has dropped their noodles

Some of the goods sold at the market were transported from other areas of China on camels in caravans along the **SILK ROAD**, which was actually made up of many different roads running across Central Asia from Northwest China.

During the Ming dynasty, people paid in coins and paper money. For bigger purchases, they might have used silver. To work out payments, people used an **ABACUS**, which was a kind of very early calculator with wooden beads on thin wooden rails.

9

The FORBIDDEN CITY

Tom found himself surrounded by people in bright silk robes, waiting in front of an enormous red gate. A door in the gate opened and Tom spotted a flash of orange. Digby!

Tom followed the people through the door and gasped at the gardens and buildings inside.

The **FORBIDDEN CITY** was built during the rule of the third Ming dynasty emperor, known as the **YONGLE EMPEROR**. It took more than a million workers 14 years to build.

Most of the buildings were painted red to symbolise power and happiness, and the roofs were made of yellow tiles, which symbolised earth and new life. Walls, pillars and furniture were decorated with dragons as a sign of the emperor's strength.

CAN YOU SPOT?
- Digby the cat
- A man on a horse
- A woman on a swing
- A giraffe
- Tom
- A worker painting the roof
- A woman flying a kite

The emperor and his family went to worship at the Temple of Heaven, which was not far from the Forbidden City. People believed in three religions: **CONFUCIANISM**, which taught people to show respect; **DAOISM**, which taught people to live in harmony with nature; and **BUDDHISM**, which taught people to give up all earthly desires.

Inside the Forbidden City, there were 980 buildings, including a zoo for exotic animals, while the courtyards could hold up to 100,000 people.

No one could go into the Forbidden City without permission, but it was usually filled with the emperor's family, friends, soldiers and servants.

HALL OF PRESERVING HARMONY

Tom followed the people towards an amazing building. Inside, a grand **BANQUET** was taking place and an important-looking man in a yellow gown sat in a grand throne.

Just then, Tom spotted Digby sneaking off with a piece of someone's dinner!

The Hall of Preserving Harmony was the most beautifully decorated building in the Forbidden City. During banquets, guests ate expensive foods like goose, lamb and chicken with rice, which was rare in Beijing because rice mainly grew in southern China. Tea was a favourite drink, sipped from delicate porcelain bowls.

During banquets, the court **ORCHESTRA** played music. The orchestra played a variety of instruments, including the **LUTE**, harp, flute and drum. They were joined by dancers.

CAN YOU SPOT?

- A woman playing a drum
- Tom
- A guest who has fallen off their chair
- Digby the cat
- A woman holding a fan
- A servant carrying a big plate of food
- The Yongle Emperor in his yellow and gold robes

Members of the **IMPERIAL COURT** wore expensive clothes made of silk. Women plucked their eyebrows and wore elaborate jewellery made of jade and gold. Men wore special belt hooks and buckles made from gold and silver.

SILK WORKSHOP

Tom chased Digby all the way back across the Forbidden City and through a pair of big red gates.

A guard shouted, but Tom didn't look back until he spotted Digby slipping inside a building on a quiet street. He crept inside to find a room filled with fabric and some very strange furniture.

Silk was the most expensive of Chinese goods. It was created by **SILKWORMS** and was then taken to workshops where it was woven on a loom, dyed different colours and embroidered. The silk was turned into beautiful clothes, handkerchiefs, wallets and belts.

CAN YOU SPOT?

- Someone in a bit of a tangle
- Tom
- Someone admiring a handkerchief
- Digby the cat
- A piece of silk decorated with a dragon
- A woman carrying a big basket of silk on her head
- Some kittens sleeping in a basket

Some colours and styles of silk were only allowed to be worn by the emperor and his court, including the colour yellow and anything with gold embroidery.

China made a lot of money selling their precious silk abroad. To protect this special trade, anyone who smuggled the silkworms out of the country would be severely punished.

DOCTOR'S SURGERY

Tom left the silk workshop and followed Digby until he reached a strange, small building. It was filled with wooden drawers, pots and bundles of herbs in different shapes and sizes. In the corner of the room, he saw a man having needles put into his body!

Suddenly, Digby sprang out from behind some shelves and raced away.

During the Ming dynasty, it was believed that people became ill if there was an imbalance in their bodies. To become well again, they went to visit a doctor or a medicine maker called an **APOTHECARY** to restore their balance.

Doctors also used a treatment called **ACUPUNCTURE**. This was where doctors put needles in special parts of the patient's body to ease pain and cure illnesses. It is still used today!

Both doctors and apothecaries treated patients using herbs and plants, which could be bought from herbal medicine shops. **MULBERRIES** were used for dizziness and **BUGBANE** was given to people with a cold.

CAN YOU SPOT?
- Someone trying some horrible-tasting herbal medicine
- Digby the cat
- A woman with an earache
- Tom
- A man having acupuncture
- A woman with twins
- A child standing on a chair

Homes

Tom chased Digby down winding roads until he reached a big house. Suddenly, he spotted his naughty cat in the arms of a woman.

"Excuse me," called Tom, but she didn't seem to hear him and walked inside. Tom hurried after her . . .

Traditional Chinese houses had overhanging roofs made of decorated tiles. This protected the home from bad weather and was also believed to ward away evil spirits.

Families enjoyed playing games together, including chess and card games.

Most homes had courtyards. The inner courtyard was for the main family and they slept in the main building. In the outer courtyard, there were guest rooms and sometimes a library.

CAN YOU SPOT?
- A woman cooking
- Digby the cat
- Tom
- Two people playing a board game
- An old woman telling a story
- A sleeping dog
- A child who has broken a vase

Most families lived on a diet of vegetables and beans with rice or **MILLET**. Food was chopped up in small pieces before it was cooked, so people ate with **CHOPSTICKS** instead of knives and forks.

PRINTING FACTORY

Digby wriggled out of the woman's arms and shot past Tom into the street. Tom followed him until he reached a large factory.

Inside, he found a lot of busy people and pieces of paper decorated with beautiful **CALLIGRAPHY**.

Suddenly, he spotted a trail of inky paw prints leading outside!

CAN YOU SPOT?

- Tom
- Someone who has spilled some ink
- Digby the cat
- Three friends chatting
- A trail of inky paw prints
- Two people engraving blocks of wood
- A printer taking a nap

The Chinese invented paper, long before the Ming dynasty, from silk rags. Over time, they found other ways to make it, using **BAMBOO** and a type of plant called **HEMP**.

During the Ming dynasty, big printing factories were built to print novels, information books and religious texts. Books became much cheaper than they had ever been before, and normal people could buy them as well as the rich.

To create a book, Chinese writing was **ENGRAVED** back-to-front on blocks of wood, then the woodblocks were covered in ink and pressed on paper. These sheets of paper were folded and stitched together, before being glued into a cover.

GRAND CANAL

Tom followed Digby's inky paw prints until he reached a canal. A fisherman eyed him suspiciously from a small boat. Digby hated the water – Tom knew he wouldn't stick around here for long!

Just then, Tom heard a familiar meow.

The Grand Canal was built to link China's two great rivers, the Yangzi River and the Yellow River. It allowed food, goods, messages and soldiers to be transported more easily.

Fishermen used simple rafts to fish on the canal. They often tied black fishing birds called **CORMORANTS** to the rafts to catch the fish for them. They put rings around their necks so the birds couldn't swallow the fish.

During the Ming dynasty, the Grand Canal was made bigger and better than ever before, including building new canal locks. It took more than three million **PEASANTS** to build the canal and half of them died from the hard work.

Wealthy people had beautifully decorated boats and they enjoyed travelling along the canal in them. There were also water taxis which took people from one side to the other.

CAN YOU SPOT?
- A wealthy family travelling on a grand boat
- Digby the cat
- A fisherman who has fallen in
- Tom
- A child surrounded by birds
- A cat looking for some fish
- An escaped cormorant

FARMLAND

Tom followed Digby's meows until he found himself standing in a big field. All around him people were hard at work, digging with spades and **PLOUGHING** the land with cattle.

In the distance, Tom spotted a dog chasing after an orange cat. Digby! Tom pelted after him.

During the Ming dynasty, farmers' lives were better than before because Emperor Hongwu had grown up as a peasant farmer. Hongwu gave lots of land to poor farmers, which gave them more space to grow food, so they could earn more money.

Once farmers had gathered the grain, they used a hand-powered **WINNOWING** machine to remove the husks, before crushing the grain with a **TILT HAMMER**, which was a bit like a see-saw with a large hammer head at one end.

CAN YOU SPOT?

• Someone carrying two baskets of grain
• Digby the cat
• A cat and her kittens
• Tom
• A farmer having a tea break
• A peacock
• A farmer who is stuck in the mud

Many people lived outside of the city and made a living working in the fields, growing millet, hemp and wheat. They used cattle or **BUFFALO** to plough the soil and a variety of **IRRIGATION** machines to water the land.

Farmers usually wore loose clothes made from hemp, which were cheaper and more practical than the clothes the rich wore.

CERaMICS FaCTORY

Tom ran until he reached a building filled with pots, vases and ornaments in all shapes and sizes.

Suddenly there was a crash and Tom turned around just in time to spot Digby racing out from behind a huge vase . . .

CaN YOU SPOT?

- Tom
- A broken vase
- Someone covered in clay
- A man carrying three vases
- Digby the cat
- Someone who has fallen into a pot
- A painter who has spilled their paint

The Ming dynasty was famous for its **PORCELAIN** ceramics. Workers mixed ground china-stone with china-clay and baked it in a very hot oven called a **KILN** . Then they painted it, usually in a blue-and-white pattern.

Porcelain was expensive to make. The kilns had to be heated up to a very high temperature and hundreds of workers were needed to do all the different jobs, from making and painting the porcelain to packing and transporting it overseas.

During the Ming era, potters developed new ways to make the porcelain as thin and shiny as possible. This meant it was very fragile.

Lots of porcelain was sold to Europe, where it was extremely popular. Factories in England even started producing their own porcelain in the Chinese style.

OPERA HOUSE

Tom followed Digby through a crowd of people into a beautifully decorated building.

Inside, he found himself in a theatre. People in strange costumes and face paint were singing and dancing on the stage. But where was Digby?

During the Ming dynasty, a type of theatre performance called Kunqu Opera became very popular. It involved a combination of acting, singing, dancing and acrobatics. Actors wore impressive costumes and painted their faces, and music was provided by an **ENSEMBLE** made up of flutes, lutes and **PERCUSSION** instruments.

CAN YOU SPOT?
- Someone too shy to go on stage
- Digby the cat
- An actor dancing with a purple fan
- Tom
- A boy who has fallen off his chair
- A headdress that has fallen off
- Someone playing a lute

The performances were very popular with rich and educated scholars, known as the **LITERATI**, as well as with ordinary peopl Opera writers had to be very careful. If plays were ever seen to be **CRITICAL** of the emperor, they could lose their heads!

LANTERN FESTIVAL

...m left the theatre in search of his naughty cat. he ...d at the evening sky and gasped in delight. The ...was filled with glowing lanterns.

Suddenly, Tom heard a familiar purr.

And there, in front of him, was Granny Bea holding Digby!

The Lantern Festival, also known as the Yuanxiao Festival, is held at the end of the Chinese New Year and celebrates family, community and the coming of spring. It first started in the **HAN DYNASTY** (206 BC–AD 220) and is still celebrated today.

Acrobats performed to the crowds and there were also magic shows and people setting off **FIRECRACKERS**. Street sellers sold delicious treats such as sweet rice balls and little cakes and sweets.

CAN YOU SPOT?

- Tom
- An acrobat standing on his hands
- Someone who has broken their lantern
- Digby the cat
- Someone eating sweet rice balls
- A frog puppet on a stick
- A cat that has been scared by a firecracker

The largest Lantern Festival in history was during the early Ming dynasty and it lasted ten whole days. Each family made their own lanterns from bamboo and paper or silk.

Lanterns were traditionally red to symbolise good fortune and happiness. The person who made the lantern would write a **RIDDLE** and put it inside the lantern. Whoever solved the riddle won a gift.

Home

Tom ran up to Granny Bea and gave her a huge hug.

As he did, there was a sudden . . . **WHOOSH!**

. . . and just like that, Tom was home!

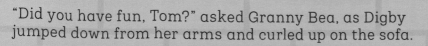

"Did you have fun, Tom?" asked Granny Bea, as Digby jumped down from her arms and curled up on the sofa.

"It was an amazing adventure!" said Tom, taking off his green robes.

"It was indeed," said Granny Bea. "And after all that excitement, I think we need a cup of tea!"

Can you go back and spot Granny Bea in every scene?

SOLUTIONS

THE GREAT WALL
Pages 6–7

- A builder who has fallen asleep
- Tom
- A misbehaving ox
- Digby the cat
- Someone having a ride in a wheelbarrow
- A bird stealing someone's lunch
- A person waving from a signal tower

THE MARKET
Pages 8–9

- Tom
- Someone using an abacus
- A woman carrying a melon on her head
- A child chasing a dog
- Digby the cat
- A food seller playing a pellet-drum
- Someone who has dropped their noodles

The FORBIDDEN CITY
Pages 10–11

- Digby the cat
- A man on a horse
- A woman on a swing
- A giraffe
- Tom
- A worker painting the roof
- A woman flying a kite

HALL OF PRESERVING HARMONY
Pages 12–13

- A woman playing a drum
- Tom
- A guest who has fallen off their chair
- Digby the cat
- A woman holding a fan
- A servant carrying a big plate of food
- The Yongle Emperor in his yellow and gold robes

SILK WORKSHOP
Pages 14–15

- Someone in a bit of a tangle
- Tom
- Someone admiring a handkerchief
- Digby the cat
- A piece of silk decorated with a dragon
- A woman carrying a big basket of silk on her head
- Some kittens sleeping in a basket

DOCTOR'S SURGERY
Pages 16–17

- Someone trying some horrible-tasting herbal medicine
- Digby the cat
- A woman with an earache
- Tom
- A man having acupuncture
- A woman with twins
- A child standing on a chair

SOLUTIONS (continued)

HOMES
Pages 18–19

- A woman cooking
- Digby the cat
- Tom
- Two people playing a board game
- An old woman telling a story
- A sleeping dog
- A child who has broken a vase

PRINTING FACTORY
Pages 20–21

- Tom
- Someone who has spilled some ink
- Digby the cat
- Three friends chatting
- A trail of inky paw prints
- Two people engraving blocks of wood
- A printer taking a nap

GRAND CANAL
Pages 22–23

- A wealthy family travelling on a grand boat
- Digby the cat
- A fisherman who has fallen in
- Tom
- A child surrounded by birds
- A cat looking for some fish
- An escaped cormorant

FARMLAND
Pages 24–25

- Someone carrying two baskets of grain
- Digby the cat
- A cat and her kittens
- Tom
- A farmer having a tea break
- A peacock
- A farmer who is stuck in the mud

CERAMICS FACTORY
Pages 26–27

- Tom
- A broken vase
- Someone covered in clay
- A man carrying three vases
- Digby the cat
- Someone who has fallen into a pot
- A painter who has spilled their paint

OPERA HOUSE
Pages 28–29

- Someone too shy to go on stage
- Digby the cat
- An actor dancing with a purple fan
- Tom
- A boy who has fallen off his chair
- A headdress that has fallen off
- Someone playing a lute

SOLUTIONS (continued)

LANTERN FESTIVAL
Pages 30–31

- Tom
- An acrobat standing on his hands
- Someone who has broken their lantern
- Digby the cat
- Someone eating sweet rice balls
- A frog puppet on a stick
- A cat that has been scared by a firecracker

Glossary

ABACUS A kind of early calculator with wooden beads on thin wooden rails

ACUPUNCTURE A treatment where a doctor puts needles in special parts of the patient's body to ease pain and cure illnesses

APOTHECARY A person who made and sold medicine

ARCHAEOLOGIST Someone who studies history by digging up and examining historical objects

BAMBOO A tall plant with hard, hollow stems, often used to make tools and furniture

BANQUET A large celebratory feast shared by many people

BUDDHISM A religion that teaches the importance of achieving an inner peace and wisdom, and encourages people to give up all earthly desires

BUFFALO A large cow-like animal with long, curved horns

BUGBANE A plant of the buttercup family with creamy yellow flowers

CALLIGRAPHY Decorative handwriting

CHOPSTICKS A pair of thin sticks, held between thumb and fingers, that are used for eating

CONFUCIANISM A religion that teaches people to achieve perfection by showing respect and kindness towards others.

CORMORANT A black, long-necked sea bird that was used for fishing during the Ming dynasty

CRITICAL Saying that someone or something is wrong

CROSSBOW A weapon, used for hunting and in war, with a small, powerful bow that is fixed across a wooden support and aimed like a gun

DAOISM A religion that teaches people to live a simple and balanced life in harmony with nature

EMPEROR A ruler of a royal empire or dynasty

ENGRAVED Cut or carved on to a hard object, such as a woodblock

ENSEMBLE A group of actors, musicians or dancers who perform together

FIRECRACKER A loud, explosive firework

FORBIDDEN CITY A palace complex in Beijing, built during the Ming dynasty for the **EMPEROR** and his household to live in.

GARRISONS A group of troops stationed in a fortress or town to defend it

HALL OF PRESERVING HARMONY One of the three halls of the Outer Court of the **FORBIDDEN CITY**

HAN DYNASTY The second dynasty in China, founded by Emperor Gaozu, which lasted from 206 BC to AD 220

HEMP A herb that can be used to make paper and clothing

IMPERIAL COURT The extended royal household of the **EMPEROR**

IRRIGATION The supply of water to land to help crops grow

KILN A special oven for firing pottery

LITERATI A group of well-educated people who are interested in literature

LUTE A guitar-like instrument with a pear-shaped body, a long neck and a vaulted back

MILLET A cereal crop that is grown for its seeds

MULBERRIES A small purple fruit grown from a mulberry tree

ORCHESTRA A group of musicians who play many different instruments together

PEASANT A poor person who works on the land

PERCUSSION Musical instruments that you play by hitting them with your hand or an object

PLOUGHING To loosen or turn up the soil with a plough before sowing seeds or planting

PORCELAIN A delicate, white and slightly translucent substance made by heating a special type of clay in a **KILN**

RIDDLE A puzzle question that has to be solved

SILK ROAD An ancient network of trade routes which connected the East and West

SILKWORM The larva of the Chinese silkworm moth that spins a silk cocoon

TEMPLE OF HEAVEN A complex of religious buildings, visited by the Emperors of the Ming dynasty for annual ceremonies of prayer to heaven for good harvest

TILT HAMMER A heavy hammer which is tilted up and then allowed to drop

WINNOWING The blowing of air through grain in order to remove the chaff, or husks

YONGLE EMPEROR The third **EMPEROR** of the Ming dynasty, who reigned from 1402 until 1424, and the son of Emperor Hongwu

Index